CW00676375

CLASSIC BLUES
Playalong *for* Tenor Saxophone

WISE PUBLICATIONS
London/New York/Paris/Sydney/Copenhagen/Madrid/Tokyo

Exclusive distributors
Music Sales Limited
14/15 Berners Street, London W1T 3LJ
Music Sales Pty Limited
120 Rothschild Avenue, Rosebery, NSW 2018, Australia

Order No. AM966702
ISBN 0-7119-8419-0
This book © Copyright 2000 by Wise Publications.

Book design by Michael Bell Design.
Music arranged by Paul Honey.
Music processed by Enigma Music Production Services.
Cover photography by George Taylor.
Printed in the United Kingdom by Page Bros., Norwich, Norfolk.

CD produced by Paul Honey.
Instrumental solos by John Whelan.
Engineered by Kester Sims.

Your Guarantee of Quality:
As publishers, we strive to produce every book to
the highest commercial standards.
The music has been freshly engraved and the book has been
carefully designed to minimise awkward page turns and
to make playing from it a real pleasure.
Particular care has been given to specifying acid-free, neutral-sized
paper made from pulps which have not been elemental chlorine bleached.
This pulp is from farmed sustainable forests and was
produced with special regard for the environment.
Throughout, the printing and binding have been planned to
ensure a sturdy, attractive publication which should give years of enjoyment.
If your copy fails to meet our high standards,
please inform us and we will gladly replace it.

Music Sales' complete catalogue describes thousands of
titles and is available in full colour sections by subject,
direct from Music Sales Limited.
Please state your areas of interest and send a
cheque/postal order for £1.50 for postage to:
Music Sales Limited, Newmarket Road, Bury St. Edmunds, Suffolk IP33 3YB.

www.musicsales.com

Saxophone Fingering Chart

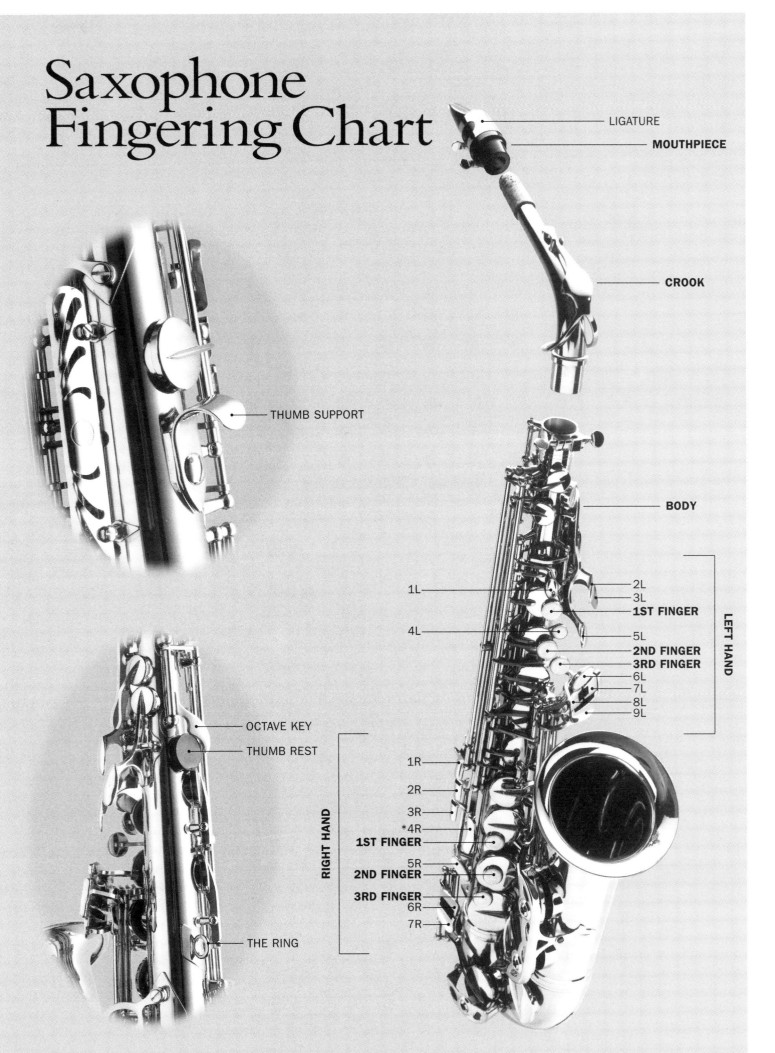

LIGATURE

MOUTHPIECE

CROOK

THUMB SUPPORT

BODY

OCTAVE KEY

THUMB REST

THE RING

1L
2L
3L
1ST FINGER
4L
5L
2ND FINGER
3RD FINGER
6L
7L
8L
9L

LEFT HAND

1R
2R
3R
*4R
1ST FINGER
5R
2ND FINGER
3RD FINGER
6R
7R

RIGHT HAND

* Not fitted on some saxophones

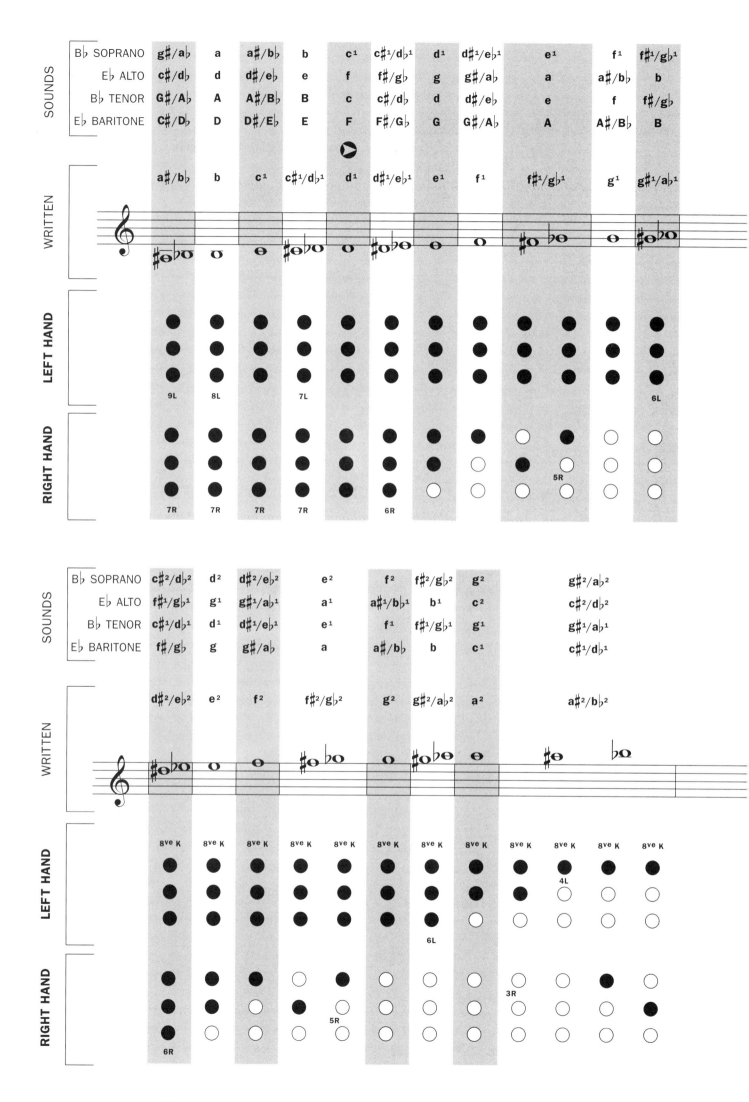

Indicates the lower limit of the best playing range

g¹ · g♯¹/a♭¹ · a¹ · a♯¹/b♭¹ · b¹ · c²

c¹ · c♯¹/d♭¹ · d¹ · d♯¹/e♭¹ · e¹ · f¹

g · g♯/a♭ · a · a♯/b♭ · b · c¹

c · c♯/d♭ · d · d♯/e♭ · e · f

a¹ · a♯¹/b♭¹ · b¹ · c² · c♯²/d♭² · d²

8ᵛᵉ K   8ᵛᵉ K

4L

3R   2R   7L

7R

a² · a♯²/b♭² · b² · c³ · c♯³/d♭³ · d³ · d♯³/e♭³

d² · d♯²/e♭² · e² · f² · f♯²/g♭² · g² · g♯²/a♭²

a¹ · a♯¹/b♭¹ · b¹ · c² · c♯²/d♭² · d² · d♯²/e♭²

d¹ · d♯¹/e♭¹ · e¹ · f¹ · f♯¹/g♭¹ · g¹ · g♯¹/a♭¹

b² · c³ · c♯³/d♭³ · d³ · d♯³/e♭³ · e³ · f³

8ᵛᵉ K   8ᵛᵉ K   8ᵛᵉ K   8ᵛᵉ K   8ᵛᵉ K   8ᵛᵉ K   8ᵛᵉ K   8ᵛᵉ K   8ᵛᵉ K   8ᵛᵉ K

1L   1L

3L   2L   2L   2L   1L

3L   3L   3L   5L

2R   1R   1R

Indicates the upper limit of the best playing range

Cry Me A River

Words & Music by Arthur Hamilton

Slow (♩ = 69)

Double tempo

Fever

Words & Music by John Davenport & Eddie Cooley

Medium tempo (♩ = 120)

To Coda ⊕

Swung ♪'s

D. %: al Coda

CODA

God Bless The Child

Words & Music by Arthur Herzog Jr. & Billie Holiday

Slow medium (♩ = 78)

Hit The Road Jack

Words & Music by Percy Mayfield

Medium tempo ($\quad = 126$)

Harlem Nocturne

Music by Earle Hagen

Medium slow ($\quarternote$ = 82)

Li'l Darlin'

Music by Neal Hefti

Medium slow ($\quarternote = 80$)

I Wish I Knew How It Would Feel To Be Free

Music by Billy Taylor

D. %: al Coda

$\oplus$ **CODA**

'Round Midnight

Music by Cootie Williams & Thelonious Monk

Swingin' Shepherd Blues

Music by Moe Koffman

D.S. al Coda

⊕ CODA

Moonglow

Words & Music by Will Hudson, Eddie de Lange & Irving Mills

Medium swing ($\quad$ = 120)

More sax appeal...

Step into the spotlight with these great additions to the Guest Spot series.

Playalong with the superb backing tracks on the specially recorded CD... follow the top line arrangements for tenor saxophone in the accompanying book.

Swing

Ten big swing numbers...

Ain't Nobody Here But Us Chickens
Flying Home
Hit That Jive Jack
I'm Getting Sentimental Over You
Is You Is Or Is You Ain't My Baby?
Jump, Jive An' Wail
Perdido
Swing That Music
Tuxedo Junction
Zoot Suit Riot

Order No. AM959618

Jazz

Ten great jazz standards...

A Night In Tunisia
Bernie's Tune
Fly Me To The Moon (In Other Words)
One Note Samba (Samba De Uma Só)
Opus One
Satin Doll
Slightly Out Of Tune (Desafinado)
Straight No Chaser
Take The 'A' Train
Yardbird Suite

Order No. AM966779

Check out these superb music compilations for saxophone...

Go Solo! Jazz
Discover solo improvisation for tenor sax with the help of recordings and backing tracks. Six great standards including All The Things You Are, Satin Doll and Walkin' Shoes. Book and CD: Order No. AM90062

100 No.1 Hits
The ultimate rock and pop collection...100 hits that have topped the British charts, specially arranged for saxophone, with chord symbols. Order No. AM90130

100 Solos: Saxophone
This outstanding collection of saxophone solos, featuring popular music and famous light classics, is ideal for players of all standards. The pieces are complete in themselves, requiring no piano accompaniment. Order No. AM33705

100+ Solos for Saxophone
Extend your repertoire with this memorable selection of jazz greats, pop hits, classical themes and show tunes. Order No. AM90025.

All these titles, and many more, are available from
your local music retailer, or in case of difficulty,
contact: Music Sales Limited, Sales & Distribution Centre,
Newmarket Road, Bury St. Edmunds, Suffolk IP33 3YB.
Tel: 01284 725725; Fax: 01284 702592
www.musicsales.com